The Best
World Cup
Trivia Book Ever

300+ Interesting Trivia Questions and Random,
Shocking, Fun Facts Every Football Fan Needs to Know

HOUSE OF BALLERS

Contents

YOUR FREE BONUS!

The 11 Most Iconic Moments in Football History

In this special edition, you'll discover the secret stories behind them.

Enjoy!

Find out by scanning the QR Code below with your smartphone:

INTRODUCTION

Football is the most widely followed sport on Planet Earth, and the FIFA World Cup, which pits the best footballing nations against one another, is its largest event. In fact, the World Cup is not just the biggest sporting event on Earth; it is simply the biggest event in the World. The final is regularly watched by billions of people, and nothing else comes close in comparison.

For one month every four years, the whole world goes to a standstill to watch the finest footballers of their generation trade battle. Hotels are booked solid; airports are parked full, bars are filled, families gather for trips, and the media world is thrown into a frenzy. When the World Cup is on, everything else stops.

The World Cup is the Superbowl, UEFA Champions League, Olympics, NBA finals, and World Series rolled into one adrenaline-charged, emotion-inducing tournament. And the World Cup has never failed to deliver on its promise.

The first World Cup was hosted and won by Uruguay in 1930. It featured only 13 teams and was markedly different from the showpiece event we now have. With 21 tournaments and 79 participating nations, the World Cup has morphed into the most eagerly awaited event in the galaxy. The current format features 32 teams drawn from an exhaustive qualification campaign that regularly features more than 200 nations. The prize money to be shared is in excess of $700 million, with the winner of the next tournament guaranteed to take home $42 million.

Only eight nations (from 13 finalists) belong to the exclusive club of winners of the world's most coveted trophy. Brazil, the home of *o Jogo Bonito* (The Beautiful Game), leads the way with five titles. Italy and Germany have four titles to their names; France, Argentina and Uruguay have two titles each; and England and Spain have solitary titles. For each triumph, dozens of nations have toiled and wept. On several occasions, revenge has been promised and attained several decades later. Bitter battles remain to be decided. Longstanding rivalries exist, never to be diluted, never to be resolved!

The history of the World Cup is filled with the extraordinary and the weird, the scintillating and the rough, gracefulness and dogmatic feats. Matches have been played against the backdrop of political tussles and wars; finals have generated tremendous shows of patriotism and nationalism. Emotions had run high such as when Zinedine Zidane defended his family's honour with a cruel headbutt; mere millimetres denied Frank Lampard the chance to pull his country level against Germany, and a mutiny disrupted the French Camp in 2010.

Football is both war and love, and the World Cup is replete with great examples of both. Pele shone as his country took three titles. Roger Milla led Cameroon on a fairy tale and entertained the world with his dancing celebrations. Just Fontaine scored 13 goals in one tournament, and more recently, Tshabalala bore an entire continent on his back as he slammed a left-footed strike into the net. And sadly, Escobar paid the ultimate price in bullets for scoring an own goal.

It is considered a great honour to be awarded the right to host the rest of the footballing world. Europe and the Americas account for the hosting of 19 of the past 21 events. From Irapuato in Mexico, Alicante in Spain, Daegu and Osaka in 2002, Durban in 2010 and Belo Horizonte in 2014, the World Cup has gone to cities all over the world. Its next stop is in the Arab world – Qatar 2022, to be precise.

The 2002 event co-hosted by South Korea and Japan was the first time Asia hosted the tourney, and it didn't disappoint. In 2010, against lowered expectations, the tournament held in South Africa proved to be perhaps the most colourful one of all time. Who could forget the loud vuvuzelas, the elusive Jabulani ball and Octopus Paul, the Seer?

The World Cup has featured some of the greatest footballers the world has ever seen, even though only 445 players have ever laid their hands on a gold medal. For many fans, a great player's legend is not complete without a great World Cup performance.

The image of the Brazilian team sinking to the ground in tears at the end of a 7-1 mauling in 2014 is forever seared into the memory of the world. Diego Maradona wrote his name into folklore forever when he had the entire English team on toast in 1986. Zinedine Zidane sent the entire Brazilian team chasing their shadows in 1998. Luka Modric cut a diminutive but irrepressible figure as he led the Croats to a place in the final at the last event. Ronaldinho announced his candidacy for the most skilful player ever against England in 2002 in a performance that ended with a red card.

In those 21 tournaments, the tales of memorable goals have been written into the stars. The world stood still as Fabio Grosso hammered a final-winning penalty into the net for Italy; Rashidi Yekini screamed and grabbed the net as he scored his country's first goal; Diego Maradona followed the controversial *Hand of God* goal with a mesmerising solo run, and Iniesta's late volley will never be forgotten in Spain.

Every World Cup features underdog stories. From Senegal defeating France in 2002, Uruguay taking Brazil to the cleaners in the *Maracanazo* 1950, to North Korea stunning Italy in 1966, the World Cup is never short of entertainment.

Stolen trophies, mutinous dressing rooms, large hearts, bribery allegations, ghost goals, controversial decisions, battles, unfulfilled potentials, nail-biting anguish, unbridled joy and ultimate triumph – the World Cup is the number one Soap Opera in history.

It is 2022!

It is time for another edition of the spectacle. Qatar controversially won the bid to host the first Winer World Cup, but there are no questions about what awaits the world. Thirty-two teams have already qualified, and a budget of $200 billion has been expended on preparations. The world cannot wait!

You need a guide, and a refresher course on the most important events in the history of the World Cup, and **this Trivia book provides just that.**

Who stunned Spain in 2018? Who discovered the stolen World Cup trophy in a bush? Why did the English press declare Maradona as *Persona non grata* in 1986? What happened at the Miracle of Bern? Why did Puskas break a bottle on Pinheiro's head in the Battle of Berne? Who fought the Battle of Santiago?

There is a lot to explore about the World Cup, and this Trivia book is your handy companion for getting ahead of the field. With 12 chapters containing 20 questions and trivia facts about everything, you can finally live your dream of being an unofficial pundit. From host nations to underdogs, from record breakers to controversial moments, the book tells the story of the World Cup in a refreshing and never seen format.

Dominate your friends with your sheer mastery of the history of the World Cup!

Become the expert at your local pub as the 2022 World Cup kicks off.

The World needs your expert analysis and knowledge about the World Cup!!!

Can you smell that?

Winter is coming, and with it also comes you, the next World Cup expert.

Pheeeeeeeeeee! Kick Off NOW!

CHAPTER

1

HOST NATIONS

"Only three people have ever silenced 200,000 people at the Maracana with a single gesture: Frank Sinatra, Pope John Paul II, and me."

- Alcides Ghiggia

20 Trivia Questions

1. Which country hosted the inaugural World Cup tournament?

    A. France

    B. Uruguay

    C. Argentina

    D. Italy

2. How many countries have hosted the FIFA World Cup more than once?

    A. 3

    B. 4

    C. 5

    D. 6

3. Who were the first ever co-hosts of the FIFA World Cup?

    A. Austria/Switzerland

    B. Poland/Sweden

    C. USA/Mexico

    D. South Korea/Japan

4. In what year was the World Cup hosted away from Europe or North/South America for the first time?

    A. 2010

    B. 2002

    C. 1994

    D. 1986

5. Including the upcoming Qatar 2022 edition, on how many occasions has the World Cup been hosted away from Europe or North/South America?

    A. 2

    B. 4

    C. 3

    D. 5

6. How many times have the World Cup hosts emerged winners?

    A. 6

    B. 3

    C. 4

    D. 5

7. Who were the first hosts to go on and win the World Cup in the same edition they hosted?

    A. Italy

    B. France

    C. England

    D. Uruguay

8. What is the shortest interval between hosting two different editions of the World Cup by the same country?

    A. 8 years

    B. 12 years

    C. 16 years

    D. 20 years

9. When did the continent of Africa host the FIFA World Cup for the first time?

    A. 2010

    B. 2006

    C. 2002

    D. 1998

10. When did Asia host the FIFA World Cup for the first time?

    A. 2006

    B. 2002

    C. 1998

    D. 2010

11. An edition of the FIFA World Cup is set to be hosted by more than two countries for the first time in _____?

    A. 2026

    B. 2030

    C. 2022

    D. 2034

12. Which stadium holds the record for the highest number of spectators at a World Cup match?

    A. Azteca Stadium

    B. Maracana Stadium

    C. Yokohama Stadium

    D. Wembley Stadium

13. How many stadiums have hosted more than one World Cup final?

    A. 3

    B. 2

    C. 5

    D. 4

14. Who were the first hosts to be eliminated in the first round of the World Cup?

    A. Japan

    B. South Korea

    C. Russia

    D. South Africa

15. Which of these countries is set to host the World Cup for a record third time in 2026?

    A. Brazil

    B. France

    C. Mexico

    D. Italy

16. Which stadium has hosted the most matches in World Cup history?

    A. Olympiastadion

    B. Stade de France

    C. Maracana Stadium

    D. Azteca Stadium

17. What city has hosted the most FIFA World Cup matches?

    A. Rome

    B. Mexico City

    C. Paris

    D. Berlin

18. How many cities have hosted more than one World Cup final?

    A. 3

    B. 2

    C. 4

    D. 5

19. On how many occasions has the World Cup been hosted in Europe?

    A. 11

    B. 12

    C. 10

    D. 13

20. Which pair of countries are set to host the 2026 World Cup along with Mexico?

    A. Honduras and Panama

    B. Costa Rica and Canada

    C. USA and Canada

    D. USA and Panama

20 Trivia Answers

1. A – Uruguay

2. C – 5

3. D – South Korea/Japan

4. B – 2002

5. C – 3

6. A – 6

7. D – Uruguay

8. C – 16 years

9. A - 2010

10. B – 2002

11. A – 2026

12. B – Maracana Stadium

13. B – 2

14. D – South Africa

15. C – Mexico

16. D – Azteca Stadium

17. B – Mexico City

18. C - 4

19. A – 11

20. C – USA & Canada

10 Fun Facts

1. A mammoth crowd of 173,850 attended the 1950 World Cup final at Brazil's Maracana Stadium. The record stands to date as the most attended match in World Cup history. The figure also represents the most for any official football match ever played.

2. In 2010, South Africa became the first ever African nation to host nation the FIFA World Cup. Unfortunately, they would also go on to become the first host nation to bow out in the first round.

3. The USA 1994 FIFA World Cup is the most attended edition of the famous competition. Over 3.5 million spectators were reported to have attended the whole showpiece, which boasted an average of 68,000 spectators per match.

4. A total of five teams have hosted the World Cup on more than one occasion. Mexico, Italy, France, Germany, and Brazil have all hosted the World Cup twice, with Mexico about to become the first nation to host three different editions in 2026.

5. USA, Canada, and Mexico have won a joint bidding right to host the 2026 edition of the FIFA World Cup. It is only the second time the World Cup has been hosted by more than one country, following the 2002 World Cup co-hosted by South Korea and Japan.

6. The 2022 FIFA World Cup in Qatar is set to become only the third edition of the storied competition to be hosted away from Europe or North/South America. The 2002 World Cup in Korea/Japan and the 2010 World Cup in South Africa are the other two World Cup editions hosted away from Europe or North South America.

7. The continent of Europe has hosted the World Cup a record 11 times. The World Cup has been hosted in North/South America 8 times, with Africa and Asia each hosting one edition of the FIFA World Cup.

8. Estadio Azteca in Mexico City, Mexico, and the Maracana in Rio de Janeiro, Brazil, are the only two stadiums in the history of the World Cup to host two different finals. Estadio Azteca also holds the record for most World Cup matches played at a particular stadium, with a total of 19 matches.

9. Uruguay was the first nation to win the World Cup as host. They beat Argentina 4-2 at Estadio Centenario, Montevideo, making that stadium the first to host a World Cup final. Italy, France, England, Germany and Argentina have also won the World Cup as hosts.

10. A total of 23 World Cup matches have taken place in Mexico City, the most any city has recorded in World Cup history. Nineteen of those games took place at Estadio Azteca, while the other four were played at Estadio Olimpico Universitario.

CHAPTER

2

WINNERS

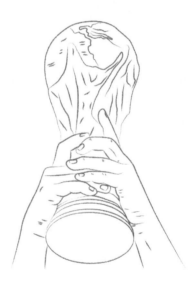

"I saw my father cry for the first time when Brazil was knocked out of the 1950 World Cup. I promised him there and then that I Would help win it for him. Seeing your side lose doesn't have to be a disaster – it could be the start of something beautiful."

- Pele

20 Trivia Questions

1. Which national team has won the most World Cups?

   A. Argentina

   B. Brazil

   C. Italy

   D. Germany

2. In what year did the Three Lions win their only World Cup?

   A. 1962

   B. 1970

   C. 1966

   D. 1958

3. What nickname is used to refer to the national team that won the 1934 and 1938 World Cups?

   A. The Albiceleste

   B. The Azzuri

   C. The Selecao

   D. The Three Lions

4. Which of the following national teams has won the World Cup twice?

   A. Mexico

   B. Spain

   C. Uruguay

   D. Belgium

5. How many teams have won consecutive editions of the World Cup?

   A. 2

   B. 3

   C. 4

   D. 1

6. Which continent has the record for most teams that have won the World Cup?

   A. Africa

   B. Europe

   C. South America

   D. Asia

7. Which of these national teams won all seven matches on the way to winning its last World Cup?

   A. Germany

   B. Brazil

   C. France

   D. Italy

8. Which team scored exactly eight goals on their way to winning their only World Cup?

   A. Spain

   B. Portugal

   C. England

   D. Uruguay

9. On how many occasions have the eventual winners of the World Cup conceded just two goals?

    A. 3

    B. 2

    C. 4

    D. 1

10. When did two-time winners, Argentina, suffer their only penalty shootout loss?

    A. 2002

    B. 1998

    C. 2006

    D. 2010

11. Which of these multiple World Cup champions is yet to lose in a penalty shootout?

    A. Germany

    B. Italy

    C. Brazil

    D. France

12. Which of the following past winners of the World Cup has featured in the most finals?

    A. Uruguay

    B. Germany

    C. Brazil

    D. Italy

13. Which of these former World Cup champions has lost the most penalty shootouts?

    A. Brazil

    B. Germany

    C. Italy

    D. Argentina

14. What is the longest interval between two World Cup triumphs by the same team? Which team was involved?

    A. 40 years, Brazil

    B. 48 years, Germany

    C. 44 years, Italy

    D. 42 years, Brazil

15. How many teams have won the World Cup just once?

    A. 5

    B. 4

    C. 3

    D. 2

16. How many World-Cup titles have been won by European nations?

    A. 12

    B. 6

    C. 16

    D. 7

17. How many countries in South America have won the World Cup?

    A. 2

    B. 3

    C. 1

    D. 7

18. How many teams have won multiple editions of the World Cup?

    A. 6

    B. 2

    C. 4

    D. 3

19. How many European nations are World Cup winners?

    A. 5

    B. 1

    C. 3

    D. 4

20. How many teams have won the World Cup courtesy of a penalty shootout victory?

    A. 2

    B. 3

    C. 4

    D. 5

20 Trivia Answers

1. B - Brazil

2. C – 1966

3. B – The Azzuri

4. C- -Uruguay

5. A – 2

6. B – Europe

7. B – Brazil

8. A – Spain

9. A – 3

10. C – 2006

11. A – Germany

12. B - Germany

13. C – Italy

14. C – 44 years

15. D - 2

16. A – 12

17. B – 3

18. A – 6

19. A – 5

20. A – 2

    21.

10 Fun Facts

1. The Brazil national team, nicknamed the *Selecao*, has won a record five World Cups, followed closely behind by Germany and Italy on four triumphs each. Argentina, Uruguay, and France have each won the World Cup twice.

2. Two World Cup finals have been decided by penalty shootouts. Roberto Baggio's infamous miss handed Brazil its fourth triumph at the USA 1994 final. Twelve years later, Italy edged France on penalties to become World champions for the fourth time.

3. South American nations Uruguay, Brazil, and Argentina are the only World Cup winners that are not from the continent of Europe. The nine triumphs between the three nations fall just short of the 12 recorded by countries from Europe.

4. Italy became the first team to retain the World Cup in 1938, following on from their success on home soil four years prior. Brazil replicated the feat with consecutive World Cup successes in 1958 and 1962.

5. Spain scored just 8 goals on their way to winning the 2010 World Cup, the first hosted on the African continent. That tally represents the lowest scored by any World Cup champion at a single tournament.

6. None of Brazil's 5 World Cup triumphs has come on home soil despite having hosted the tournament on two occasions. The Selecao lost to Uruguay in their first ever World Cup final when they hosted the 1950 edition before crashing out in the semifinals 64 years later at the same venue.

7. Following successes at consecutive World Cups in 1934 and 1938, the *Azzurri* of Italy had to wait 44 years for their next title, the longest period between two World Cup triumphs by the same national team.

8. The Three Lions of England and Spain's *La Furia Roja* are the only one-time winners of the World Cup. Six other national teams have won the competition on two or more occasions.

9. Four-time world champions, Germany, have never lost a penalty shootout in a World Cup match. Fellow four-time winners Italy in contrast, have lost three penalty shootouts, the joint most in World Cup history.

10. The trophy given out to the winners of the World Cup was known as the Jules Rimet Trophy, named after the Frenchman who put forth the idea for the tournament's creation. This trophy was permanently gifted to then three-time champions Brazil (1958, 1962, 1970) in 1970. A new trophy named the "FIFA World Cup" became the new prize in 1974.

CHAPTER

3

GOALKEEPERS

"They won't remember me for winning the World Cup; it'll be for that save. That's how big a thing it is. People just want to talk about that save."

- Gordon Banks

20 Trivia Questions

1. What World Cup record do goalkeepers Peter Shilton and Fabian Barthez share?

   A. Most minutes played

   B. Most clean sheets

   C. Most penalties saved

   D. Most penalties conceded

2. Which English goalkeeper conceded the "Hand of God" goal to Maradona?

   A. Joe Hart

   B. David Seaman

   C. Gordon Banks

   D. Peter Shilton

3. Which goalkeeper conceded the most goals in a single World Cup match?

   A. Luis Guevara Mora

   B. Peter Rufai

   C. Jens Lehmann

   D. Andre Onana

4. What World Cup record does Italian goalkeeper Walter Zenga proudly own?

   A. Most minutes without receiving a card

   B. Most minutes without committing a foul

   C. Most minutes without conceding a goal

   D. Most minutes without conceding a penalty

5. What record do Antonio Carbajal and Mohamed Al-Deayaa jointly hold?

   A. Most goals conceded

   B. Most saves

   C. Most penalties saved

   D. Most fouls

6. What was the nationality of the goalkeeper that conceded the most goals in a single World Cup match?

   A. El Salvador

   B. Nigeria

   C. Mexico

   D. Germany

7. Which World Cup-winning nation did Giampiero Combi captain?

   A. Argentina

   B. Italy

   C. Brazil

   D. France

8. How many keepers have kept more clean sheets at the World Cup than Peter Shilton?

   A. 0

   B. 5

   C. 2

   D. 3

9. Who is the youngest keeper to save a penalty in normal time at a World Cup match?

   A. Danijel Subasic

   B. Iker Casillas

   C. Jens Lehmann

   D. Essam El-Hadary

10. New Zealand's Richard Wilson went 921 minutes without conceding a goal in the 1982 World Cup qualifying matches. How many clean sheets did he keep in that run?

    A. 4

    B. 15

    C. 7

    D. 9

11. Who was in goal for Ukraine during their shootout victory against Switzerland at the 2006 World Cup?

    A. Ilian Meslier

    B. Oleksandr Shovkovskyi

    C. Petr Cech

    D. Andriy Lunin

12. How many keepers have conceded more World Cup goals than Mexico's Antonio Carbajal?

    A. 2

    B. 0

    C. 5

    D. 4

13. The best goalkeeper at the 1974 World Cup was famous for thwarting England. Who was he?

    A. Jan Tomaszewski

    B. Emerson Leao

    C. Sepp Maier

    D. Jan Jongbloed

14. The most memorable save of this England keeper's career was against Pele at the 1970 World Cup. Who was he?

   A. Peter Shilton

   B. Gordon Banks

   C. David James

   D. David Seaman

15. At the age of 40, which World Cup-winning national team did Dino Zoff captain?

   A. England

   B. West Germany

   C. Argentina

   D. Italy

16. What is the nationality of the only starting goalkeeper that won consecutive World Cups?

   A. Italy

   B. Brazil

   C. Uruguay

   D. Mexican

17. Sepp Maier made four consecutive World Cup squads for West Germany. When did he win the tournament?

   A. 1982

   B. 1986

   C. 1974

   D. 1978

18. Who is the first goalkeeper to be substituted at the World Cup for any reason other than injury?

    A. Kazadi Mwamba

    B. Carlos Kameni

    C. Rene Higuita

    D. Jorge Campos

19. Which national team substituted its goalkeeper for the first time at a World up for a reason other than injury?

    A. Australia

    B. Zaire

    C. Norway

    D. Cameroun

20. Which country did the first African goalkeeper save a penalty play for?

    A. Morocco

    B. Tunisia

    C. Algeria

    D. Egypt

20 Trivia Answers

1. B – Most clean sheets

2. D – Peter Shilton

3. A – Luis Guevara Mora

4. C – Most minutes without conceding a goal

5. A – Most goals conceded

6. A – El Salvador

7. B – Italy

8. A – 0

9. B – Iker Casillas

10. D – 9

11. B – Oleksandr Shovkovskyi

12. B – 0

13. A – Jan Tomaszewski

14. B – Gordon Banks

15. D – Italy

16. B – Brazil

17. C – 1074

18. A – Kazandi Mwamba

19. B – Zaire

20. D – Egypt

10 Fun Facts

1. Egyptian goalkeeper Essam El-Hadary is the oldest player to ever feature in a World Cup match. His appearance against Saudi Arabia at the Russia 2018 World Cup broke Faryd Mondragon's record. He also saved a penalty in that match to become the first African goalkeeper to save a World Cup penalty.

2. United States of America Men's national team goalkeeper Tim Howard's 16 saves against Belgium at the Brazil 2014 World Cup is the most for a single World Cup match.

3. Goalkeepers Fabian Barthez, Gianluigi Buffon, and Iker Casillas share the record for the least amount of goals conceded at a World Cup by the eventual winners. With each of the aforementioned trio conceding a miserly tally of just two goals.

4. Fabian Barthez and Peter Shilton have both recorded ten clean-sheets at the World Cup, the most in the history of the competition. Barthez was part of the French team that went all the way in 1998, while Shilton conceded the "Hand of God" goal to Diego Maradona.

5. Italian goalkeeper, Walter Zenga, did not allow a goal for 517 minutes during the 1990 World Cup, the longest a keeper has ever gone without conceding a goal at the World Cup. He picked up five clean-sheets within that span.

6. Luis Guevara Mora conceded the most goals in a single World Cup game when his El Salvador team lost 10-1 against Hungary in the two sides' opening game of the 1982 World Cup.

7. Saudi Arabian keeper Mohamed Deayaa and his Mexican counterpart Antonio Carbajal have each let in a record 25 goals at the World Cup. Antonio Carbajal, however, appeared in a record five World Cup tournaments.

8. Polish Jan Tomaszewski and American Brad Friedel are the only two keepers to save two penalties at a single World Cup tournament. Spanish Iker Casillas also saved two World Cup penalties, albeit at different tournaments.

9. Switzerland goalkeeper Pascal Zuberbuhler did not concede a single goal from open play at the 2006 World Cup. His team lost 3-0 on penalties to Ukraine in the Round of 16.

10. South Korean goalkeeper Hong Duk-Yung conceded the most goals at a single World Cup tournament., letting in 16 during the 1954 World Cup.

CHAPTER

4

DEFENDERS

"It's funny that as soon as I retired from international football, Italy won the World Cup."

- Paolo Maldini

20 Trivia Questions

1. What is the record for appearances made by a defender at the World Cup?

    A. 11 games

    B. 15 games

    C. 23 games

    D. 32 games

2. What is the nationality of the only defender to appear in 5 different World Cups?

    A. Mexico

    B. Spain

    C. Germany

    D. Italy

3. Which defender has appeared in the most World Cup matches?

    A. Rafael Marquez

    B. Philip Lahm

    C. Paolo Maldini

    D. Cafu

4. The fastest yellow card in World Cup history was received by _____

   A. Jesus Corona

   B. Jesus Gallardo

   C. Jose Batista

   D. Rigobert Song

5. The recipient of the fastest red card in World Cup history was from which national team?

   A. Uruguay

   B. Argentina

   C. Brazil

   D. Mexico

6. Which of these defenders has been sent off more than once at the World Cup?

   A. Sergio Ramos

   B. Rigobert Song

   C. Marcel Desailly

   D. Harry Maguire

7. Which of the following defenders has been to five World Cup tournaments?

   A. Philip Lahm

   B. Paolo Maldini

   C. Wladyslaw Zmuda

   D. Rafael Marquez

8. The recipient of the World Cup's fastest yellow card is a defender of which nationality?

   A. El Salvador

   B. Mexico

   C. Honduras

   D. Costa Rica

9. The only defender to receive two red cards at the World Cup was from _____?

    A. Uruguay

    B. France

    C. Cameroon

    D. Brazil

10. Which defender netted Spain's only goal in their semifinal victory against Germany at the 2010 World Cup?

    A. Sergio Ramos

    B. Gerard Pique

    C. Carles Puyol

    D. Carlos Marchena

11. Which defender scored the winning goal at the 1990 World Cup final?

    A. Andreas Brehme

    B. Roberto Ayala

    C. Pedro Monzon

    D. Jurgen Kohler

12. Who was the first defender to be sent off in a World Cup final?

    A. Oscar Ruggeri

    B. Jose Serrizuela

    C. Juan Simon

    D. Pedro Monzon

13. Which defender captained Brazil to 1970 World Cup success in Mexico?

    A. Zico

    B. Carlos Alberto Torres

    C. Everaldo

    D. Cafu

14. In which World Cup final did Argentina defender Roberto Sensini concede a penalty?

    A. 2018

    B. 1978

    C. 2006

    D. 1990

15. Which of these Italian defenders never won the World Cup?

    A. Alessandro Nesta

    B. Paolo Maldini

    C. Marco Materazzi

    D. Fabio Cannavaro

16. Cafu made 124 appearances for the Brazil national team. How many of those were at the World Cup?

    A. 6

    B. 20

    C. 12

    D. 26

17. Which World Cup-winning team was Gaetano Scirea part of?

    A. Brazil

    B. Italy

    C. Argentina

    D. France

18. Which England defender's memorable tackle won the ball off of Jairzinho at the 1970 World Cup?

    A. Bobby Moore

    B. Jack Charlton

    C. Norman Whiteside

    D. Tony Adams

19. Which of these defenders scored the fastest own goal in World Cup history?

    A. Sead Kolasinac

    B. Emir Spahic

    C. Nicolas Otamendi

    D. Marcos Rojo

20. In which World Cup did Colombian defender Andres Escobar score an infamous own goal?

    A. 2002 World Cup

    B. 1998 World Cup

    C. 1994 World Cup

    D. 1986 World Cup

20 Trivia Answers

1. C – 23 games

2. A – Mexico

3. C – Paolo Maldini

4. B – Jesus Gallardo

5. A – Uruguay

6. B – Rigobert Song

7. D – Rafael Marquez

8. B – Mexico

9. C – Cameroon

10. C – Carles Puyol

11. A – Andreas Brehme

12. D – Pedro Monzon

13. B – Carlos Alberto Torres

14. D – 1990

15. B – Paolo Maldini

16. D – 20

17. B – Italy

18. A – Bobby Moore

19. A – Sead Kolasinac

20. C – 1994 World Cup

10 Fun Facts

1. Legendary Italian defender Paolo Maldini has played in more World Cup matches than any other defender. He appeared for the Azzuri 23 times between 1990 and 2002, finishing runner-up in 1990 and 1994.

2. Mexican defender Rafael Marquez is one of only four players to feature in five different editions of the World Cup. He made 19 appearances at the World Cup, the most for his country, between 2002 and 2018.

3. Bosnia & Herzegovina defender Sead Kolasinac scored the fastest own goal in World Cup history when he put it into his own net after just two minutes and ten seconds in a group stage match against Argentina at the Brazil 2014 World Cup.

4. Having come on as a second-half substitute, Pedro Monzon was shown a red card for a high tackle on Germany's Jurgen Klinsmann during the 1990 World Cup final, making Monzon the first player to receive his marching orders in a World Cup final.

5. Legendary English defender, Bobby Moore, inspired the Three Lions to their only World Cup triumph on home soil in 1966. Four years later, his brilliant tackle won the ball off the superbly talented Jairzinho; a memorable moment believed to have inspired generations of English defenders.

6. Cameroun defender, Rigobert Song, is the only defender to receive more than one red card at the World Cup. The two red cards he has been shown are the most for any player, with France midfielder Zinedine Zidane also getting sent off twice.

7. Following a stellar showing at the Germany 2006 World Cup, which ended with him lifting the trophy for Italy, Fabio Cannavaro became just the third defender to be awarded the prestigious Ballon d'Or award.

8. In a Group E match against Scotland at the 1986 World Cup, Uruguayan defender, Jose Batista, got sent off after just 56 seconds, making his dismissal the earliest in any World Cup match ever played.

9. Mexican defender, Jesus Gallardo, was shown the fastest yellow card in the history of the World Cup just 13 seconds into his side's final group game against Sweden at the 2018 World Cup.

10. Argentina defender, Roberto Sensini, conceded the penalty that cost his side the 1990 World Cup following a sliding tackle on Germany's Rudi Voller. German defender Andreas Brehme converted the spot kick to secure West Germany's third World Cup title.

11. Brazil defender Cafu is the only player to make an appearance in 3 different World Cup finals. The legendary right-back featured in the Selecao's triumphs in 1994 and 2002 against Italy and Germany, respectively, as well as in their defeat against France in 1998.

CHAPTER

5

MIDFIELDERS

"Consequently, I won just about everything I set out to win, everything but the World Cup, of course. But even now, I don't regret that because I was part of a team which twice reached the semifinals."

- Michel Platini

20 Trivia Questions

1. Which of these German midfielders has played the most matches at the World Cup?

    A.   Michael Ballack

    B.   Lothar Matthaus

    C.   Wolfgang Overath

    D.   Mesut Ozil

2. How many times did Zinedine Zidane play for France at the 2002 World Cup?

    A.   2

    B.   3

    C.   1

    D.   4

3. How many goals did Xavi Hernandez score for Spain at the World Cup?

    A.   0

    B.   4

    C.   7

    D.   2

4. Which of these midfielders has been to the most World Cup tournaments?

    A. Xavi Hernandez

    B. Bastian Schweinsteiger

    C. Andrea Pirlo

    D. Lothar Matthaus

5. Francesco Totti's only World Cup goal for Italy came against which of these teams?

    A. France

    B. Australia

    C. Ukraine

    D. Germany

6. Which of these Italy midfielders made the most World Cup appearances for the Azzuri?

    A. Gennaro Gattuso

    B. Andrea Pirlo

    C. Alessandro Del Piero

    D. Francesco Totti

7. Argentina midfielder Esteban Cambiasso scored his only World Cup goal at the_____?

    A. 2002 World Cup

    B. 2006 World Cup

    C. 2010 World Cup

    D. 2014 World Cup

8. How many goals did Yaya Toure score in his 9 World Cup appearances for Ivory Coast?

   A. 0

   B. 1

   C. 2

   D. 3

9. Which of these Nigerian midfielders never scored a goal at the World Cup?

   A. Jay-jay Okocha

   B. Sunday Oliseh

   C. Wilson Oruma

   D. Finidi George

10. Only one of these renowned African players played at a World Cup. Who was it?

    A. Stephen Appiah

    B. Abedi Pele

    C. Seydou Keita

    D. Mohamed Aboutrika

11. Which of these England midfielders played the most matches for the Three Lions at the World Cup?

    A. Declan Rice

    B. Frank Lampard

    C. Paul Scholes

    D. David Beckham

12. Which of these Russian midfielders scored the most goals at the 2018 World Cup?

    A. Yuri Zhirkov

    B. Denis Cheryshev

    C. Andrey Arshavin

    D. Alan Dzagoev

13. Maksym Kalynychenko was a goal scorer for which national team at the 2006 World Cup?

    A. Poland

    B. Ukraine

    C. Sweden

    D. Czech Republic

14. Against which of these teams was Portuguese midfielder Deco sent off at the 2006 World Cup?

    A. England.

    B. Netherlands

    C. Germany

    D. France

15. Which midfielder set up Iniesta's winning goal at the 2010 World Cup final?

    A. Marcos Senna

    B. Xabi Alonso

    C. Cesc Fabregas

    D. Pedro

16. All of these Brazilian midfielders have scored a goal in the World Cup final except

    A. Jairzinho

    B. Zito

    C. Gerson

    D. Didi

17. In which edition of the World Cup did Diego Maradona receive a red card?

    A. 1982

    B. 1986

    C. 1998

    D. 1994

18. Brazil midfielder Ronaldinho scored a goal and then got sent off in a single match at the 2002 World Cup. Who were the opponents?

    A. Turkey

    B. England

    C. Costa Rica

    D. China

19. Which of these midfielders has scored the most goals at the World Cup?

    A. Mesut Ozil

    B. James Rodriguez

    C. Thomas Muller

    D. Diego Maradona

20. Which England midfielder got sent off for kicking Argentina's Diego Simeone at the 1998 World Cup?

    A. Paul Scholes

    B. David Beckham

    C. Paul Merson

    D. Steve McManaman

20 Trivia Answers

1. B – Lothar Matthaus

2. C – 1

3. A – 0

4. D – Lothar Matthaus

5. B – Australia

6. C – Alessandro Del Piero

7. B – 2006 World Cup

8. B – 1

9. A - Jay-jay Okocha

10. A – Stephen Appiah

11. D – David Beckham

12. B – Denis Cheryshev

13. B – Ukraine

14. B – Netherlands

15. C – Cesc Fabregas

16. D – Didi

17. A – 1982

18. B – England

19. C – Thomas Muller

20. B – David Beckham

10 Fun Facts

1. The Brazilian midfielder, Ronaldinho, received his marching orders just seven minutes after scoring what was arguably one of the most incredible goals in World Cup history. His mistimed challenge on Danny Mills resulted in a red card moments after he had completed a turnaround for his side in their quarterfinal tie against England.

2. Mexican midfielder, Andres Guardado, has been to four different World Cup tournaments. Should he be selected for the Qatar 2022 edition, he will become the fifth player overall and the third from Mexico to go to the World Cup five times.

3. Lothar Matthaus has played at a record five World Cup tournaments and featured in a record 25 matches. He captained West Germany to World Cup success in 1990, having been on the losing side in the two previous finals.

4. South Korean Hong Myung-bo was the first Asian player to play in four successive editions of the World Cup. He led his country to a historic fourth-place finish in 2002 on home soil, converting the winning penalty in a shootout victory against Spain in the quarterfinal.

5. David Beckham turned from hero of the final group game to villain in England's Round-of-16 match against Argentina at the 1998 World Cup. His petulant kick on Diego Simeone got him sent off, leaving England a man down for nearly the entirety of the second half. England went on to lose 4-3 on penalties.

6. Diego Maradona received his solitary World Cup red card when he kicked Brazil's Batista during a World Cup Second Round match in 1982. He redeemed himself four years later by guiding the Albiceleste to World Cup success in Mexico.

7. Argentinian midfielder, Luis Monti, played in two World Cup finals for two different teams. He lost the final in 1930 to Uruguay, playing for his native Argentina, before ending up on the victorious Italian side four years later due to his Romagnol ancestry.

8. Midfielders Robert Prosinecki and Robert Jarni featured for Yugoslavia in 1990 and Croatia in 1998. The duo, along with Luis Monti and Ferenc Puskas, are the only players to play for more than one team in World Cup history.

9. Northern Ireland's Norman Whiteside is the youngest player to be involved in a World Cup match. At 17 years and 41 days old, his debut against Yugoslavia at the 1982 World Cup broke Pele's record, which had stood for 24 years.

10. Brazil winger, Denilson, made 11 appearances as a substitute in the 1998 and 2002 World Cups. No other player has had as much in the history of the competition.

CHAPTER

6

STRIKERS

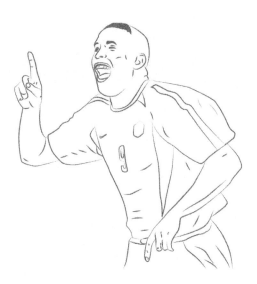

"I'm sure sex wouldn't be as rewarding as winning the World Cup. It's not that good, but the World Cup is every four years, and sex is not."

- Ronaldo Nazário de Lima

20 Trivia Questions

1. Miroslav Klose scored his record-breaking 16th World Cup goal against which of these teams?

    A. Argentina

    B. Brazil

    C. Netherlands

    D. Italy

2. Just Fontaine's first World Cup hat-trick came against which of these teams?

    A. Yugoslavia

    B. Northern Ireland

    C. West Germany

    D. Paraguay

3. Which of these Brazilian forwards injured France captain Robert Jonquet at the 1958 World Cup?

    A. Garrincha

    B. Vava

    C. Pele

    D. Joel

4. How many World Cup matches did Carlos Caszely play for Chile?

    A. 2

    B. 3

    C. 4

    D. 5

5. All of these players have scored at least once at four different World Cups except
    _____

    A. Pele

    B. Miroslav Klose

    C. Cristiano Ronaldo

    D. Lionel Messi

6. Hungary striker Laszlo Kiss scored three goals as a substitute in a single match. Who were the opponents?

    A. El Salvador

    B. Honduras

    C. Belgium

    D. Argentina

7. In which edition did Laszlo Kiss score the World Cup's fastest hat-trick?

    A. 1970 World Cup

    B. 1978 World Cup

    C. 1982 World Cup

    D. 1986 World Cup

8. Which of these forwards has scored hattricks at more than one World Cup tournament?

    A. Harry Kane

    B. Gerd Muller

    C. Gabriel Batistuta

    D. Just Fontaine

9. How many players have scored successive World Cup hattricks?

   A. 2

   B. 0

   C. 4

   D. 5

10. What World Cup record does Russian forward Oleg Salenko hold?

   A. Most hattricks

   B. Fastest goal

   C. Most goals in a single match

   D. Most goals against the same opponent

11. Which of these strikers has the most goals in World Cup qualification matches?

   A. Ali Daei

   B. Cristiano Ronaldo

   C. Carlos Ruiz

   D. Robert Lewandowski

12. Polish forward Ernest Willmowski scored four goals in his country's 5-6 loss to which of these teams?

   A. Brazil

   B. France

   C. Italy

   D. Uruguay

13. Apart from Hungary, which other national team did Ferenc Puskas play for?

   A. West Germany

   B. Italy

   C. Spain

   D. Argentina

14. Pele's first World Cup hattrick came when he was

    A.   16 years old

    B.   18 years old

    C.   17 years old

    D.   19 years old

15. Which of these players scored the most goals in a single World Cup qualifying match?

    A.   Archie Thompson

    B.   Carlos Ruiz

    C.   Ali Daei

    D.   Kazuyoshi Miura

16. Which of these legends scored the only hat-trick in a World Cup final?

    A.   Pele

    B.   Geoff Hurst

    C.   Gerd Muller

    D.   Just Fontaine

17. How many goals has Germany striker Gerd Muller scored at the World Cup?

    A.   12

    B.   13

    C.   14

    D.   15

18. How many players have scored more World Cup goals than Brazil's Ronaldo?

    A.   0

    B.   1

    C.   4

    D.   3

19. Who is England's highest goalscorer at the World Cup?

    A. Geoff Hurst

    B. Gary Lineker

    C. Harry Kane

    D. Michael Owen

20. In which edition of the World Cup did Italy forward Roberto Baggio's infamous penalty miss happen?

    A. 1982 World Cup

    B. 1990 World Cup

    C. 1994 World Cup

    D. 2002 World Cup

20 Trivia Answers

1. B – Brazil

2. D – Paraguay

3. B – Vava

4. C – 4

5. D – Lionel Messi

6. A – El Salvador

7. C – 1982 World Cup

8. C – Gabriel Batistuta

9. A – 2

10. C – Most goals in a single match

11. C – Carlos Ruiz

12. A – Brazil

13. C – Spain

14. C – 17 years old

15. A – Archie Thompson

16. B – Geoff Hurst

17. C – 14

18. B – 1

19. B – Gary Lineker

20. C – 1994 World Cup

10 Fun Facts

1. Germany's Miroslav Klose has the most top 3 finishes at the World Cup. The German striker did not finish outside of the top 3 at four World Cups between 2002 and 2014. He won the World Cup in 2014, finished runner-up in 2002, and had third-placed finishes in 2006 and 2010. He is the only player with four World Cup medals, and his tally of 16 World Cup goals is unmatched.

2. Argentinian striker, Attilio Demaria, was part of two different World Cup final squads. Demaria was part of the Argentina squad that lost the 1930 final and also part of the Italy squad that emerged winners in 1934. Unlike Luis Monti, however, Demaria played neither of the two finals.

3. Brazilian strikers Pele and Vava are the only players to score in two different World Cup finals and end up on the winning team on both occasions. Vava scored in the 1958 and 1962 final wins for Brazil, while Pele found the net in the 1958 and 1970 finals.

4. Brazil's Pele remains the only player to be part of three World Cup-winning teams. His medal for the 1962 win was awarded retroactively by FIFA in 2007 as he only played the first two matches of that tournament.

5. West Germany striker, Karl-Heinz Rummenigge, is the only player to lose two World Cup finals as captain. His team faltered at the final hurdle at the 1982 and 1986 World Cups against opponents Italy and Argentina, respectively.

6. German striker, Miroslav Klose, has taken part in 14 World Cup knockout matches and 17 World Cup wins, both stats the most recorded by any player in World Cup history.

7. Brazilian forward Edu is the youngest ever player to be named to a World Cup squad. He made the Brazil 1966 World Cup squad at the age of 16 years and 339 days.

8. French Striker, Just Fontaine, scored 13 goals in 6 matches at the 1958 World Cup, including a remarkable four goals against holders West Germany. No player has scored as many in a single World Cup tournament.

9. Hungary's Sandor Koscis (1954), France's Just Fontaine (1958), and West Germany's Gerd Muller (1970) are the only players to score two hattricks at a single World Cup tournament. Argentina's Gabriel Batistuta scored a hattrick at the 1994 World Cup and repeated the feat four years later.

10. Chilean striker Carlos Caszely was the first player to be shown a red card at a World Cup match. Matchday referee Dogan Babacan sent him off during the opening match of the 1974 World Cup against West Germany.

CHAPTER

7

BREAKOUT STARS

"As a kid growing up in the back streets of Dublin, I used to pretend I was playing in the World Cup with my mates out on the streets, and now I will be doing it for real."

- Robbie Keane

20 Trivia Questions

1. Which of these Sweden players earned a penalty against South Korea at the 2018 World Cup?

    A. Emil Forsberg

    B. Sebastian Larsson

    C. Viktor Claesson

    D. Albin Ekda

2. Which of these opponents did Cho Hyun-woo keep a clean sheet against at the 2018 World Cup?

    A. Germany

    B. Sweden

    C. Mexico

    D. Senegal

3. Which of these players is the youngest African to score a World Cup goal?

    A. Moussa Wague

    B. El Hadji Diouf

    C. Nwankwo Kanu

    D. Emmanuel Adebayor

4. Which Uruguayan completed more passes than any player aged 23 or under at the Russia 2018 World Cup?

    A. Lucas Torreira

    B. Luis Suarez

    C. Rodrigo Bentacur

    D. Cristian Rodriguez

5. Which goalkeeper earned the man of the Match award for his display against Brazil at the 2014 World Cup group stage?

    A. Jose Corona

    B. Guillermo Ochoa

    C. Stipe Pletikosa

    D. Jasper Cillessen

6. Who scored the volley that was named the best goal of the 2014 World Cup?

    A. Neymar

    B. Lionel Messi

    C. Cristiano Ronaldo

    D. James Rodriguez

7. Siphiwe Tshabalala of South Africa scored the first goal of the 2010 World Cup. Who were the opponents?

    A. Mexico

    B. Uruguay

    C. France

    D. Republic of Ireland

8. Which of these players scored the most goals for Germany at the 2010 World Cup?

    A. Gerd Muller

    B. Bastian Schweinsteiger

    C. Thomas Muller

    D. Miroslav Klose

9. On the back of a superb showing at the 2010 World Cup, one of these players earned a move to Real Madrid from Werder Bremen. Who was he?

    A. Toni Kroos

    B. Mesut Ozil

    C. Sami Khedira

    D. Christoph Metzelder

    1. Who was Ghana's top goalscorer at the 2010 World Cup?

    A. Kevin-Prince Boateng

    B. Asamoah Gyan

    C. Sulley Muntari

    D. Stephen Appiah

10. How many goals did World Cup debutant Luis Suarez score at the 2010 World Cup?

    A. 3

    B. 4

    C. 5

    D. 2

11. Germany's Lukas Podolski scored his first World Cup goal against which of these teams?

    A. Sweden

    B. Ecuador

    C. Italy

    D. Portugal

12. Which Dutch defender scored against Spain and made the Team of the Tournament at the 2014 World Cup?

    A. Ron Vlaar

    B. Stefan de Vrij

    C. Bruno Martins Indi

    D. Daley Blind

13. Which national team did Keylor Navas star for at the 2014 World Cup?

    A. Honduras

    B. Costa Rica

    C. Panama

    D. Mexico

14. In what edition of the World Cup did Landon Donovan come into the limelight with goals against Poland and Mexico?

    A. 2006 World Cup

    B. 2002 World Cup

    C. 1998 World Cup

    D. 2010 World Cup

15. How many goals did Joel Campbell score during Costa Rica's impressive run to the quarterfinals at the 2014 World Cup?

    A. 1

    B. 2

    C. 3

    D. 4

16. How many goals did England's World Cup debutant Michael Owen score at the 1998 World Cup?

    A. 5

    B. 4

    C. 3

    D. 2

17. Marc Overmars burst onto the scene at the 1994 World Cup. How many goals did he score for the Dutch national team?

    A. 0

    B. 2

    C. 3

    D. 1

18. Which of these France defenders scored a stunning volley for his first World Cup goal against Argentina at the 2018 World Cup?

    A. Lucas Hernandez

    B. Benjamin Pavard

    C. Raphael Varane

    D. Samuel Umtiti

19. How many goals did England's Paul Gascoigne score at the 1990 World Cup?

    A. 2

    B. 1

    C. 0

    D. 3

20 Trivia Answers

1. C – Viktor Claesson

2. A – Germany

3. A – Moussa Wague

4. C – Rodrigo Betancur

5. B – Guillermo Ochoa

6. D – James Rodriguez

7. A- Mexico

8. C – Thomas Muller

9. B – Mesut Ozil

10. B – Asamoah Gyan

11. A – 3

12. B – Ecuador

13. B - Stefan de Vrij

14. B – Costa Rica

15. B – 2002 World Cup

16. A – 1

17. C – 3

18. A – 0

19. B – Benjamin Pavard

20. C – 0

10 Fun Facts

1. Having spent much of South Korea's 2018 World Cup qualifying campaign as the third-choice goalkeeper, Cho Hyun-woo's remarkable form for K-League team Daegu prompted his promotion to the first choice. He quickly repaid the faith with a string of fine displays, including a memorable performance in his side's 2-0 win over Germany.

2. Benjamin Pavard's belter of a goal against Argentina at the 2018 World Cup Round of 16 made him the first defender to score for France's senior side since Lilian Thuram at the 1998 World Cup.

3. Juan Fabian Quintero dropped the gauntlet at the feet of compatriot and 2014 World Cup star James Rodriguez with a number of impressive performances for Colombia at the 2018 World Cup group stage. He set up goals for his teammates in games against Poland and Senegal before scoring a delightful freekick in his side's surprise 1-2 loss to Japan.

4. Mexico's World Cup debutant Hirving Lozano scored the only goal of their opening Group F win against defending champions Germany at the 2018 World Cup. He also crucially set up Javier Hernandez's winner in the second game that all but ensured Mexico's passage to the knockout round.

5. Merely weeks after sealing a free transfer to Spanish top flight side Real Betis, Japan's Takashi Inui put in a number of sterling performances at the 2018 World Cup, including a sweet 25-yard strike that at one point seemed to be enough to ease Japan past Belgium in the Round Of 16.

6. South Africa's Siphiwe Tshabalala became the first African player to score a World Cup goal on African soil when his well-hit left-footed strike from a distance found the back of opponent Mexico's net in the opening game of the 2010 World Cup.

7. Touted as the heir to Michael Ballack, who got injured on the eve of the 2010 World Cup, Thomas Muller scored five goals, the joint most, to go along with three assists that helped Germany finish a respectable third at the 2010 World Cup.

8. Mesut Ozil's playmaking ability caught the attention of the watching world as the World Cup debutant helped Germany cruise to the 2010 World Cup semifinals with relative ease before bowing out to eventual winners Spain.

9. Asamoah Gyan scored three out of Ghana's four goals at the 2010 World Cup as the Black Stars tethered on the edge of a first semifinal appearance for an African side before Gyan's late penalty miss after Luis Suarez handled a goal-bound shot gave Uruguay the chance to progress on penalties.

10. Philip Lahm burst onto the international scene at the 2006 World Cup held in his homeland. He scored the first goal in Germany's opening group game against Costa Rica and was impressive throughout as Germany finished third.

CHAPTER

8

CONTROVERSY

"A little with the hand of Maradona, a little with the hand of God"

- Diego Armando Maradona

20 Trivia Questions

1. England referee Graham Poll made a mistake and showed a yellow card three times to the same player before sending him off. Who was the player?

   A. Marko Babic

   B. Josip Simunic

   C. Darijo Srna

   D. Niko Kovac

2. In what World Cup edition were four red cards and sixteen yellow cards shown during a feisty Portugal vs Netherlands Round-of-16 clash?

   A. 2002 World Cup

   B. 2006 World Cup

   C. 1998 World Cup

   D. 1994 World Cup

3. Patrick Battison suffered a damaged vertebra and lost two teeth following a collision in the 1982 World Cup semifinal. Who did he collide with?

   A. Harald Schumacher

   B. Manfred Kaltz

   C. Bernd Forster

   D. Uli Stielike

4. Italy defender Marco Materazzi was controversially sent off against which of these opponents at the 2006 World Cup?

   A. France

   B. Germany

   C. Ukraine

   D. Australia

5. In which of these countries was the Jules Rimet trophy stolen for the second time?

   A. England

   B. Brazil

   C. Italy

   D. France

6. Frank Lampard had a controversially disallowed goal against Germany at the 2010 World Cup. What was the scoreline when he scored?

   A. 1-0

   B. 2-1

   C. 3-1

   D. 4-1

7. Under the orders of Benito Mussolini, Italy wore black shirts against which of these teams at the 1938 World Cup?

   A. Hungary

   B. France

   C. Brazil

   D. Norway

8. Luis Suarez has been at the centre of a few controversial events. Which of these Italians did he appear to bite at the 2014 World Cup?

    A. Leonardo Bonucci

    B. Mattia de Sciglio

    C. Andrea Barzagli

    D. Giorgio Chiellini

9. Brazil's Ronaldo fell sick on the eve of a 1998 World Cup match against which of these teams?

    A. Chile

    B. Netherlands

    C. Denmark

    D. France

10. Diego Maradona failed a drug test at which of these World Cup tournaments?

    A. 1990 World Cup

    B. 1994 World Cup

    C. 1998 World Cup

    D. 1986 World Cup

11. The infamous 'Disgrace of Gijon' happened at which World Cup tournament?

    A. 1982 World Cup

    B. 1986 World Cup

    C. 1990 World Cup

    D. 1978 World Cup

12. Which pair of teams were the victims of poor officiating in knockout matches against South Korea at the 2002 World Cup?

    A. Turkey and Germany

    B. Spain and Portugal

    C. Spain and Italy

    D. USA and Poland

13. In what year did FIFA controversially award Qatar the hosting rights for the 2022 World Cup?

    A. 2020

    B. 2010

    C. 2012

    D. 2014

14. Who handled the ball in the build-up to William Gallas' goal against the Republic of Ireland that sent France to the 2010 World Cup?

    A. Nicolas Anelka

    B. Thierry Henry

    C. Frank Ribery

    D. Florent Malouda

15. In what year did the infamous 'Battle of Santiago' occur?

    A. 1966

    B. 1962

    C. 1970

    D. 1958

16. The Republic of Ireland coach Mick McCarthy had a bust up one of his players at the 2002 World Cup. Which player was that?

    A. Robbie Keane

    B. Roy Keane

    C. Shay Given

    D. John O'Shea

17. Which French star was abruptly sent home from the 2010 World Cup?

    A. Florent Malouda

    B. Patrice Evra

    C. Nicolas Anelka

    D. Jeremy Toulalan

18. Who national team was embroiled in a mutinous 2010 World Cup campaign?

    A. Nigeria

    B. France

    C. Switzerland

    D. Mexico

19. During which World Cup did the infamous 'Battle of Nurnberg' take place?

    A. 1998 World Cup

    B. 2002 World Cup

    C. 2006 World Cup

    D. 2010 World Cup

20. Which national team fired its head coach a day before the start of the 2018 FIFA World Cup?

    A. Argentina

    B. Spain

    C. South Korea

    D. Poland

20 Trivia Answers

1. **B – Josip Simunic**

2. **B – 2006 World Cup**

3. **A – Harald Schumacher**

4. **D – Australia**

5. **B – Brazil**

6. **B – 2-1**

7. **B – France**

8. **D – Giorgio Chiellini**

9. **D – France**

10. **A – 1994 World Cup**

11. **C – 1982 World Cup**

12. **B – Spain & Italy**

13. **B – 2010**

14. **B – Thierry Henry**

15. **B – 1962**

16. **B – Roy Keane**

17. **C – Nicolas Anelka**

18. **B – France**

19. **C – 2006 World Cup**

20. **B - Spain**

10 Fun Facts

1. Andres Escobar's own goal in Colombia's 1-2 loss at the 1994 World Cup against the host did not go down well with fans back at home, particularly those affiliated with the cartels in Escobar's hometown of Medellin. The cartels had apparently staked heavy sums on the outcome of the game. Upon the defender's return home following Colombia's elimination in the first round, he was tragically murdered outside a nightclub by suspected cartel members.

2. The Jules Rimet World Cup trophy was stolen four months ahead of the 1966 World Cup while the prize was on exhibition at Westminster Central Hall in London. It was later found by David Corbett and his dog named Pickles in a bush. After it was permanently awarded to Brazil, the trophy was then stolen once again and has not been found to this day.

3. During the extra time of a hotly contested 2010 World Cup quarterfinal, Uruguay managed to stop two goal-bound efforts from Ghana's Stephen Appiah and Dominic Adiyah in quick succession. But the referee spotted an infringement and blew for a penalty. Replays indicated that Uruguay forward Luis Suarez had stopped the second attempt on the line with his hand. He was thus shown a red card for the handball. Ghana's Asamoah Gyan, who had been his side's talisman in the tournament, lined up the penalty shot for a chance to send his country to the semifinals. He sent the goalkeeper the wrong way but crashed the resulting penalty against the crossbar, sending Suarez into wild celebrations near the tunnel. Uruguay eventually won 4-2 on penalties.

4. Marco Materazzi had just cancelled out Zinedine Zidane's goal as the 2006 World Cup final approached its closing stages. As Zidane walked away from a failed France attack, he suddenly turned back and headbutted Materazzi, an event that resulted in his sending off and the culmination of his illustrious career. It was later reported that Materazzi had insulted Zidane's sister, provoking the

Frenchman's violent reaction. In one of the most iconic World Cup moments of all time, Zinedine Zidane walked past the World Cup trophy, head bowed, as he went down the tunnel. France went on to lose the final.

5. In the 51st minute of England's 1986 World Cup quarterfinal against Argentina, Diego Maradona appeared to use his hand to steer an aerial ball into the back of England goalkeeper Peter Shilton's net. Maradona would later confirm the incident, calling it 'The Hand of God." He scored one more in the tie, a wonderful jinking run that is arguably the greatest goal ever scored in World Cup history to drag his side past England truly. However, the *Hand of God* incident understandably generated a lot of attention.

6. Mexican referee Byron Moreno, and his Egyptian counterpart, Gamal Al-Ghandour, were forced to retire shortly after the 2002 World Cup for their abysmal performances in matches involving co-hosts South Korea.

7. During the 1966 World Cup final, matchday referee Gottfried Dienst consulted his linesman before awarding a goal to Geoff Hurst for his shot that crashed against the underside of the crossbar and bounced down towards the West Germany goal. A similar incident occurred when the two sides met at the 2010 World Cup. With the score at 2-1 in favour of the Germans, a Frank Lampard effort that seemingly crossed the line got disallowed, prompting debate and eventual adoption of the Goal-line Technology.

8. FIFA arranged it such that the final rounds of matches from each group took place simultaneously following West Germany's farcical 1-0 win against Austria that guaranteed passage to the next rounds for both teams at the expense of Algeria, who had played its final group game a day before. That arrangement still exists to date and has been adopted in almost all cup competitions.

9. Giorgio Ferrini had to be escorted off by Police following his dismissal during the 1962 World Cup match between Chile and Italy. The game, one of the most ill-tempered in World Cup history, is famously referred to as the 'Battle of Santiago."

10. In Kuwait's sole appearance at the World Cup in 1982, France's Alain Griese's goal was disallowed simply because the Kuwaiti players had stopped playing upon hearing a whistle blown from someone among the spectators.

CHAPTER

9

MEMORABLE GAMES

"The World Cup is a very important way to measure the good players, and the great ones."

- Pelé

20 Trivia Questions

1. Which player scored the winner in Italy's 4-3 semifinal win over West Germany at the 1970 World Cup?

   A. Fabio Grosso

   B. Giovanni Rivera

   C. Camoranesi

   D. Alessandro Del Piero

2. Who scored England's consolation goal against Argentina in the 1986 World Cup quarterfinal?

   A. Michael Owen

   B. Gary Lineker

   C. Chris Waddle

   D. Sir Bobby Charlton

3. Which player scored a hattrick in Italy's thrilling 3-2 win against Brazil at the 1982 World Cup?

   A. Andrea Belotti

   B. Paolo Rossi

   C. Gianpiero Marini

   D. David Trezeguet

4. Who converted the winning penalty in the shootout following West Germany's 3-3 draw with France at the 1982 World Cup?

   A. Horst Hrubesch

   B. Michael Platini

   C. Roberto Baggio

   D. Manfred Kaltz

5. Which Brazilian player scored the consolation goal in their 1-7 defeat at the hands of Germany at the 2014 World Cup?

   A. Ramires

   B. Oscar

   C. Casemiro

   D. Fred

6. Holders Uruguay lost 2-4 to which team at the semifinal of the 1954 World Cup?

   A. Austria

   B. Hungary

   C. Norway

   D. Brazil

7. France won the penalty shootout following a 1-1 draw with Brazil in the 1986 World Cup quarterfinal. What was the scoreline of the shootout?

   A. 2-1

   B. 4-2

   C. 4-3

   D. 3-0

8. How many penalties were awarded during Argentina's 3-4 loss to France at the 2018 World Cup?

    A. 0

    B. 1

    C. 4

    D. 3

9. At which edition of the World Cup did Portugal's Eusebio score four goals in a 5-3 win over North Korea?

    A. 1998

    B. 1966

    C. 1974

    D. 1958

10. Which player scored West Germany's winner in their 3-2 final victory against Hungary at the 1954 World Cup?

    A. Helmut Rahn

    B. Michael Ballack

    C. Philip Lahm

    D. Hans Schafer

11. Goals from Rivaldo and Bebeto helped Brazil to a 3-2 victory against Denmark at which World Cup?

    A. 1994 World Cup

    B. 2006 World Cup

    C. 1998 World Cup

    D. 1990 World Cup

12. Which England player missed the decisive penalty that sent West Germany through to the final of the 1990 World Cup?

    A. Tony Adams

    B. Mark Hughes

    C. Chris Waddle

    D. David Platt

13. In the first World Cup final clash between two former champions, which player scored Brazil's last goal against Italy in 1970?

    A. Oscar

    B. Carlos Alberto

    C. Ederson

    D. Pele

14. Which player scored a hattrick for the Soviet Union in their 3-4 loss to Belgium at the 1986 World Cup?

    A. Vasili Rats

    B. Igor Belanov

    C. Zinchenko

    D. Igor Akinfeev

15. At what stage of the 1970 World Cup did West Germany rally from 0-2 down to beat England?

    A. Group stage

    B. Final

    C. Quarterfinals

    D. Semifinals

16. In the quarterfinal meeting between Argentina and Netherlands at the 1998 World Cup, which player scored a 90th-minute winner?

    A. Dennis Bergkamp

    B. Javier Saviola

    C. Edgar Davids

    D. Javier Mascherano

17. Which player scored in the first minute of Turkey's 3-2 win against South Korea in the third-place playoff at the 2002 World Cup?

    A. Heug Min Son

    B. Hakan Sukur

    C. Chong-Gug Song

    D. Emre Can

18. Which Brazil player missed his penalty during the shootout that followed the 1-1 draw with Italy at the 1994 World Cup final?

    A. Marcio Santos

    B. Roberto Carlos

    C. Ronaldo

    D. Dunga

19. Two of Argentina's three goals at the 1978 World Cup final were scored by which of these players?

    A. Mario Kempes

    B. Juan Riquelme

    C. Esteban Cambiasso

    D. Oscar Alberto Ortiz

20. Which player scored a brace during Senegal's 3-3 draw with Uruguay in the final group stage match at the 2002 World Cup?

    A. Diego Forlan

    B. Alvaro Recoba

    C. Papa Bouba Diop

    D. Khalilou Fadiga

20 Trivia Answers

1. B – Giovanni Rivera

2. B - Gary Lineker

3. B - Paolo Rossi

4. A – Horst Hrubesch

5. B – Oscar

6. B – Hungary

7. C – 4-3

8. B – 1

9. B – 1966

10. A – Helmut Rahn

11. C – 1998 World Cup

12. C – Chris Waddle

13. B – Carlos Alberto

14. B – Igor Belanov

15. C - Quarterfinals

16. A – Dennis Bergkamp

17. B – Hakan Sukur

18. A – Marcio Santos

19. A – Mario Kempes

20. C – Papa Bouba Diop

10 Fun Facts

1. Marcello Lippi's Italy scored two goals in the last two minutes of extra time to upstage tournament hosts and favourites Germany at the semifinals of the 2006 FIFA World Cup. It seemed almost certain the feisty yet entertaining clash of World Cup heavyweights would be decided on penalties before Italy's Fabio Grosso, and Alessandro Del Piero popped up with two late goals to send the eventual winners through.

2. The 2002 World Cup final was one of the most anticipated in the tournament's history. Favorites Brazil faced an impressive German team anchored by the brilliant Oliver Kahn. At the end of a hugely entertaining affair, Brazil triumphed two-nil thanks to a brilliant Ronaldo Delima performance. Brazil has not won the World Cup since then. The Qatar 2022 edition will be their next chance.

3. The Round of 16 meeting between England and Argentina had everything from goals, to two penalties awarded in the opening ten minutes, to last-ditch goal-stopping tackles and a sending-off. Alan Shearer and Michael Owen scored in quick succession to complete a turnaround for England after Gabriel Batistuta had given Argentina the lead after just six minutes. However, Javier Zanetti restored parity for the Albiceleste before halftime. England was forced to hang on for almost the entirety of the second half following David Beckham's red card in the 47th minute before Argentina prevailed 4-3 on penalties.

4. In what was a rematch of the World Cup final four years prior, the Netherlands thrashed holders Spain in the two sides' opening group match at the 2014 World Cup. It seemed business as usual for the Spanish when Xabi Alonso converted from the penalty spot to put them ahead close to the half-hour mark. But the Orange responded with an equaliser just before halftime. A masterful performance led by Arjen Robben and Robin van Persie saw the Dutch thrash

the Spaniards 5-1. This match is also famous for the iconic Flying Dutchman header from van Persie. The Spaniards never recovered and put up a shoddy defence of their title.

5. Portugal's Cristiano Ronaldo scored a hattrick that included a penalty and a stunning freekick to salvage a share of the spoils for his team in an entertaining 3-3 draw with Spain at the 2018 World Cup. Spain had clawed their way back twice and led 3-2 heading into the last five minutes before Ronaldo's freekick in the 88th minute brought Portugal level and a share of the spoils.

6. Belgium rallied back from 2-0 down in the second half to emerge 3-2 victors in an entertaining Round-of-16 match at the 2018 World Cup. Genki Haraguchi and Takashi Inui had given Japan a shock 2-0 lead within four second-half minutes before Belgium roared back through goals from Jan Vertonghen, Marouane Fellaini, and Nacer Chadli to progress into the last eight.

7. Following convincing wins against Sweden And Spain, Brazil just needed a draw to become world champions on home soil in 1950. Brazil led early through Fiaca before Uruguay completed a turnaround within the last 25 minutes of the contest to silence a large crowd of nearly 200,000 fans, most of whom were Brazilians.

8. Geoff Hurst became the only player to score a hat-trick in a World Cup final when his England side bested West Germany 4-2 in the final match of the 1966 World Cup. Hurst's goal that gave England a 3-2 lead 11 minutes into extra time has gone down as one of the most controversial in World Cup history as many believed it did not cross the goal line.

9. Brazil's array of superstars such as Pele, Jairzinho, and Rivelino made them instant favourites for the 1970 World Cup. Their 1-0 win against holders England featured two quite memorable moments; Gordon Bank's save from Pele and Bobby Moore's tackle to win the ball off Jairzinho, scorer of the game's solitary goal.

10. Two of the most memorable goals in World Cup history were scored at Mexico's Azteca Stadium during the 1986 quarterfinal clash between Argentina and England. After a goalless first half, Argentina's Diego Maradona helped a lifted ball past England keeper Peter Shilton, the infamous "Hand of God" goal, before Maradona again raced past five England defenders and the keeper to slot home what came to be known as the goal of the century.

CHAPTER

10

INDIVIDUAL AWARDS

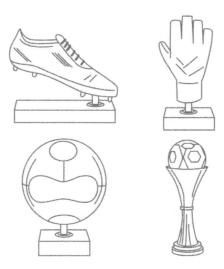

"I would change all my individual trophies for that trophy of World Cup champion."

- Luka Modric

20 Trivia Questions

1. In which World Cup edition was the Lev Yashin award for best goalkeeper first awarded?

    A. 2006 World Cup

    B. 1994 World Cup

    C. 1986 World Cup

    D. 1982 World Cup

2. The Lev Yashin award is named after Lev Yashin, a veteran goalkeeper from which of these countries?

    A. Yugoslavia

    B. Soviet Union

    C. Czechoslovakia

    D. Hungary

3. Which of the following Lev Yashin award winners never graced a World Cup final?

    A. Gianluigi Buffon

    B. Fabian Barthez

    C. Michel Preud'homme

    D. Oliver Kahn

4. Which of these keepers claimed the Golden Ball and the Yashin award at the same World Cup tournament?

    A. Fabian Barthez

    B. Gianluigi Buffon

    C. Oliver Kahn

    D. Michel Preud'homme

5. Which player was the first recipient of the Golden Ball awarded in 1982?

    A. Falcao

    B. Paolo Rossi

    C. Miroslav Klose

    D. Paul Breitner

6. In which World Cup did Zinedine Zidane win the Golden Ball award?

    A. 1998

    B. 2002

    C. 2006

    D. 2010

7. Which player was named the unofficial best player at the 1978 FIFA World Cup?

    A. Diego Maradona

    B. Mario Kempes

    C. Johann Cruyff

    D. Paolo Rossi

8. Which of these Brazilians was awarded the Silver Ball at the 2002 World Cup?

    A. Neymar

    B. Ronaldo

    C. Ronaldinho

    D. Ze Roberto

9. Who was jointly selected by France Football and L'Equipe as the Best Player of the 1966 World Cup?

    A. Eusebio

    B. Bobby Charlton

    C. Martin Demichelis

    D. Franz Beckenbauer

10. Who received the first Golden Shoe award in 1982?

    A. Zico

    B. Alan Shearer

    C. Paolo Rossi

    D. Norman Whiteside

11. How many goals were enough to land England's Gary Lineker the 1986 World Cup Golden Shoe?

    A. 3

    B. 5

    C. 6

    D. 10

12. Four players were tied on five goals at the 2010 World Cup. Who won the Golden Boot?

    A. Wesley Sneijder

    B. Thomas Muller

    C. David Villa

    D. Diego Forlan

13. All of these players scored five goals and shared the 1986 World Cup Silver Shoe except for?

    A. Emilio Butragueno

    B. Careca

    C. Diego Maradona

    D. Paul Breitner

14. Cameroun's Roger Milla shared the 1990 World Cup Bronze Shoe with which of these players?

    A. Gary Lineker

    B. Diego Maradona

    C. Lothar Matthaus

    D. Michel

15. The Golden Shoe has only ever been shared once. At which edition did this happen?

    A. 1990 World Cup

    B. 1994 World Cup

    C. 1998 World Cup

    D. 2002 World Cup

16. Which of these players was the first recipient of the Best Young Player award in 2006?

    A. Philip Lahm

    B. Lukas Podolski

    C. Lionel Messi

    D. Cristiano Ronaldo

17. France's Paul Pogba emerged as the Best Young Player at which World Cup tournament?

    A. 2006 World Cup

    B. 2010 World Cup

    C. 2014 World Cup

    D. 2018 World Cup

18. Which team won the inaugural FIFA Fair Play Trophy at the 1970 World Cup?

    A. Brazil

    B. Peru

    C. England

    D. West Germany

19. England and France shared the FIFA Fair Play Trophy at which World Cup tournament?

    A. 1990 World Cup

    B. 1994 World Cup

    C. 1998 World Cup

    D. 2002 World Cup

20. Which Country has won the FIFA Fair Play Trophy the most times?

    A. Brazil

    B. Spain

    C. England

    D. Colombia

20 Trivia Answers

1. B – 1994 World Cup

2. B – Soviet Union

3. C – Michel Prudhomme

4. C – Oliver Kahn

5. B – Paolo Rossi

6. C – 2006 World Cup

7. B – Mario Kempes

8. B – Ronaldo

9. B – Bobby Charlton

10. C – Paolo Rossi

11. C – 6

12. B – Thomas Muller

13. D – Paul Breitner

14. A – Gary Lineker

15. B – 1994 World Cup

16. B – Lukas Podolski

17. C – 2014 World Cup

18. B – Peru

19. C – 1998 World Cup

20. A - Brazil

10 Fun Facts

1. The Golden Ball award for best player and the Golden Boot award for top goalscorer have both been awarded since the 1982 World Cup in Spain. The two awards are both sponsored by sports merchandise company Adidas. The Golden Boot was named Golden Shoe between 1982 and 2006.

2. The Best Young Player award for the best player under 21 years of age at the start of the World Cup year has been awarded since the 2006 World Cup. It is currently being sponsored by car manufacturer Hyundai. Lukas Podolski won the first award in 2006.

3. The FIFA Fair Play Trophy for the team with the best disciplinary record that progressed beyond the Group Stage has been awarded since the 1970 World Cup. Peru won the inaugural award, having received no yellow or red cards at the tournament. Brazil has won the award the most times.

4. From the 2010 World Cup onwards, the Lev Yashin award for the best goalkeeper has been renamed the Golden Glove award or Adidas Golden Glove as it is also been sponsored by the sports merchandise company.

5. A Man of the Match award for the most outstanding player at each match during a World Cup tournament has been awarded since the 2002 World Cup in South Korea and Japan. Senegal's El Hadji Diouf won the first such award after his country's shock 1-0 win over holders France in the tournament's opening match.

6. Between 1994 and 2006, an All-Star team comprised of the best players selected by the FIFA Technical Study Group was announced. FIFA discontinued the practice after the 2010 World Cup.

7. Thomas Muller's three assists at the 2010 World Cup edged him ahead of his challengers for the Golden Boot as four players were tied on five goals apiece. The trio of Wesley Sneijder, Diego Forlan, and David Villa, however, all had one assist each.

8. Russia's Oleg Salenko and Bulgaria's Hristo Stoichkov both received the Golden Shoe at the 1994 World Cup, the only time the award was shared. The two players were tied on six goals apiece, and the assist tiebreaker could not still separate them as they both had one assist each. So, they both received a Golden Shoe.

9. Russia's Oleg Salenko is the only player to have won the top goalscorer award while playing for a team that did not progress beyond the Group Stage. His six goals at the 1994 World Cup, which included a five-goal salvo against Cameroun, were the only international goals the Russian ever scored.

10. Italy's Paolo Rossi (1982) and Salvatore Schillaci (1990) are the only players to have won both the Golden Shoe and the Golden Ball in the same World Cup tournament. Paolo Rossi is the only player to win both individual accolades and the World Cup in the same tournament.

CHAPTER

11

UNDERDOG STORIES

"Cameroon pushed me to play again in 1994 because they thought I was the only one who could score goals. They had no confidence in any of the other players to do so."

- Roger Milla

20 Trivia Questions

1. El Salvador beat which of these countries to qualify for the 1982 World Cup?

   A. Panama

   B. USA

   C. Canada

   D. Costa Rica

2. Having reached the quarterfinals four years prior, Senegal was beaten to the qualification spot for the 2006 World Cup by _____?

   A. Mali

   B. Liberia

   C. Togo

   D. Zambia

3. Jamaica's sole appearance at the FIFA World Cup came at which of these tournaments?

   A. 1990 World Cup

   B. 1998 World Cup

   C. 1994 World Cup

   D. 1986 World Cup

4. Italy missed out on qualification for the 2022 World Cup following a defeat to which of these teams?

    A. Gibraltar

    B. Albania

    C. Luxembourg

    D. North Macedonia

5. Which of these teams beat continental powerhouses Nigeria and Algeria to a place at the 2006 World Cup?

    A. Zimbabwe

    B. Rwanda

    C. Gabon

    D. Angola

6. Eventual 2010 World Cup winners, Spain, lost their opening game of that tournament to _____?

    A. Honduras

    B. Chile

    C. Switzerland

    D. Sweden

7. Ghana's first-ever World Cup win came against which of these teams?

    A. USA

    B. Czech Republic

    C. Serbia

    D. Australia

8. South Africa's only win at the 2010 World Cup was against which of these teams?

    A. Mexico

    B. Uruguay

    C. France

    D. New Zealand

9. Which of these players scored Italy's goal in their shock 1-2 loss to South Korea at the 2002 World Cup?

    A. Andrea Belotti

    B. Andrea Pirlo

    C. Cristian Vieri

    D. Paolo Maldini

10. Which player scored Senegal's solitary goal in their shock 1-0 victory over France in the opening game of the 2002 World Cup?

    A. Fabrice Akwa

    B. El Hadji Diouf

    C. Papa Bouba Diop

    D. Garba Lawal

11. How many players were sent off in Cameroon's surprise 1-0 win against Argentina at the 1990 World Cup?

    A. 0

    B. 3

    C. 2

    D. 1

12. Algeria's first-ever World Cup match ended in victory against which of these teams?

    A. Austria

    B. Bulgaria

    C. Chile

    D. West Germany

13. Which player scored USA's only goal in their shock win against England at the 1950 World Cup?

    A. Joe Gaetjens

    B. Frank Wallace

    C. Landon Donovan

    D. Jozy Altidore

14. The World Cup match dubbed 'The Miracle of Bern' took place at which tournament?

    A. 1962 World Cup

    B. 1950 World Cup

    C. 1954 World Cup

    D. 1958 World Cup

15. Courtesy of Pak Doo-Ik's goal, North Korea knocked out which of these teams at the 1966 World Cup?

    A. Portugal

    B. Italy

    C. Soviet Union

    D. Chile

16. Which player scored Northern Ireland's only goal in their defeat of Spain at the 1982 World Cup?

    A. Johnny Evans

    B. Robbie Keane

    C. Gerry Armstrong

    D. Norman Whiteside

17. Which of these players scored Germany's first goal in their stunning 7-1 win against Brazil at the 2014 World Cup?

    A. Andre Schurrle

    B. Sami Khedira

    C. Thomas Muller

    D. Miroslav Klose

18. Scotland defeated eventual runners-up the Netherlands at the group stage 1978 World Cup thanks to goals from Kenny Dalglish and _____?

    A. Graeme Souness

    B. Archie Gemmill

    C. Stuart Kennedy

    D. Joe Archer

19. In a 1994 World Cup Round-of-16 match, two-time champions Argentina suffered a surprise 2-3 reverse. Who were the opponents?

    A. Bulgaria

    B. Nigeria

    C. Denmark

    D. Romania

20. Which of these Spanish players missed his spot kick during the penalty shootout defeat against Russia at the 2018 World Cup?

    A. Marcos Senna

    B. Iago Aspas

    C. Roberto Soldado

    D. Andres Iniesta

20 Trivia Answers

1. **B – USA**

2. **C – Togo**

3. **B – 1998 World Cup**

4. **D – North Macedonia**

5. **D – Angola**

6. **C – Switzerland**

7. **B – Czech Republic**

8. **C – France**

9. **C – Cristian Vieri**

10. **C – Papa Bouba Diop**

11. **C – 2**

12. **D – West Germany**

13. **A – Joe Gaetjens**

14. **C – 1954 World Cup**

15. **B – Italy**

16. **C – Gerry Armstrong**

17. **C – Thomas Muller**

18. **B – Archie Gemmil**

19. **D – Romania**

20. **B – Iago Aspas**

10 Fun Facts

1. Cameroon was not expected to go far at the 1990 World Cup after being drawn into a group that included holders Argentina, Romania, and the Soviet Union. The Indomitable Lions had other ideas, however, and opened their campaign with a shock 1-0 victory over holders Argentina. A win in their second match against Romania was enough to book a Round-of-16 tie against Colombia, which they also won 2-1. The Cameroonians' dream run ended with a 2-3 defeat after extra time to Bobby Robson's England in the quarterfinal.

2. Bulgaria recovered from their opening match loss to Nigeria at the 1994 World Cup with convincing wins over Greece and Argentina, which saw them progress beyond the Group Stage for only the second time. Their fairytale run continued after knocking out Mexico on penalties following a 1-1 draw, and then they scored twice in the final 15 minutes to defeat Germany 2-1 in the quarterfinal. Eventual runners-up Italy brought an end to Bulgaria's run in the semifinal.

3. In only their third ever appearance at the World Cup, Turkey put together a string of impressive performances that saw them finish third at the 2002 World Cup. Having made it out of a group that included eventual winners Brazil, China, and Costa Rica, Turkey dispatched co-hosts Japan in the Round of 16 and then Senegal in the quarterfinal to set up a rematch with group C opponents Brazil in the semifinal. The Turks lost again to Brazil but claimed third place with a 3-2 victory over South Korea.

4. World Cup debutants, Senegal, opened their 2002 World Cup campaign with a shock 1-0 win against none other than holders France. Subsequent draws with Denmark and Uruguay were enough to get them into the Round of 16, where they defeated Sweden by two goals to one. Their fairytale run was cut short following a 1-0 loss to Turkey in the quarterfinal.

5. South Korea's brilliant run to the semifinals and a historic fourth-place finish, the best by an Asian side, was marred by refereeing controversies in their Round of 16 and quarterfinal matches against Italy and Spain, respectively. Following a spectacular group stage campaign that saw the Koreans finish top with 7 points, Italy had Francesco Totti controversially sent off in their 1-2 Round of 16 loss against the co-hosts before two Spanish goals were incorrectly ruled out for offside in a goalless draw. South Korea won 5-3 on penalties before crashing out at the hands of Germany in the semifinals.

6. Croatia made its maiden appearance at the 1998 World Cup as an independent nation following the split up from Yugoslavia. The unfancied Croatians made it all the way to the semifinals before losing out to eventual champions France. They did, however, beat the Netherlands in the third-place playoff match to win the bronze medal.

7. North Korea's maiden appearance at the World Cup in 1966 saw them go 3-0 up in the first half hour of their quarterfinal meeting with Portugal before Eusebio's four-gial salvo helped Portugal to an astonishing 5-3 comeback win that ended the North Koreans impressive run that had seen them beat Italy to progress from the group stage.

8. Costa Rica eliminated Greece on penalties in the Round of 16 at the 2014 World Cup before shootout heartbreak befell them in their first ever quarterfinal against the Netherlands. Costa Rica's run is all the more impressive considering the fact that they finished top of a group that had former champions Italy, England and Uruguay.

9. Ghana became the third African national team to reach the quarterfinals at the FIFA World Cup when the tournament was hosted in South Africa in the year 2010. The Black Stars were cruelly denied a semifinal spot when Uruguayan forward Luis Suarez stopped two goal-bound efforts in quick succession with his hand. Unfortunately for Ghana and Africa as a whole, Asamoah Gyan missed the resulting penalty.

10. New Zealand avoided defeat in its three group stage matches at the 2010 World Cup, finishing above holders Italy though they were both eliminated in the first knockout round.

CHAPTER

12

RECORD BREAKERS

*"Given the developments in modern football, it's very
unlikely that a player will still be called up for a World
Cup at the age of 42, excluding goalkeepers. That's why
I believe my goal record will stand for some time to come."*

- Roger Milla

20 Trivia Questions

1. The youngest coach in World Cup history, Juan Jose Tramutola, managed which of these teams at the 1930 World Cup?

    A. Uruguay

    B. France

    C. Argentina

    D. Algeria

2. Which of these teams have had the most unsuccessful World Cup qualification attempts?

    A. India

    B. Luxembourg

    C. Faroe Islands

    D. North Korea

3. Wales' appearance at the 2022 World Cup is set to be their first in how many years?

    A. 58 years

    B. 60 years

    C. 62 years

    D. 64 years

4. On how many occasions have the Netherlands finished in the top 3 places at the World Cup?

    A. 0

    B. 6

    C. 4

    D. 5

5. In how many tournaments has Brazil gone unbeaten?

    A. 4

    B. 5

    C. 6

    D. 7

6. Which of these teams has been to the World Cup final the most?

    A. Italy

    B. Germany

    C. Brazil

    D. Argentina

7. Which of these teams has lost as many World Cup finals as they have won?

    A. Brazil

    B. Italy

    C. Germany

    D. England

8. Which of these teams has been involved in World Cup penalty shootouts the most?

    A. England

    B. Italy

    C. Germany

    D. Argentina

9. Which of these teams has conceded the most own goals in World Cup history?

    A. Mexico

    B. Bulgaria

    C. Russia

    D. Cameroon

10. All of these teams have never scored a goal at the World Cup except

    A. Angola

    B. Trinidad and Tobago

    C. Canada

    D. China

11. All of these teams have recorded at least 20 draws at the World Cup, except

    A. Italy

    B. England

    C. Germany

    D. France

12. All of these teams have recorded more than 20 defeats in World Cup matches except

    A. Mexico

    B. Argentina

    C. Germany

    D. England

13. The World Cup's oldest goalscorer, Roger Milla, scored his last World Cup goal against which of these teams?

    A. China

    B. Russia

    C. Brazil

    D. Sweden

14. Pele became the youngest ever goalscorer at the World Cup when he scored against which of these teams?

    A. Austria

    B. England

    C. Wales

    D. Soviet Union

15. The first-ever World Cup goal was scored by which of these players?

    A. Bert McGhee

    B. Lucien Laurent

    C. Guillermo Stabile

    D. Pedro Cea

16. Which of these players has clocked the most minutes on the pitch at the World Cup?

    A. Diego Maradona

    B. Paolo Maldini

    C. Rafael Marquez

    D. Miroslav Klose

17. Which of these players has played the most World Cup games as captain of his national team?

    A. Paolo Maldini

    B. Rafael Marquez

    C. Lothar Matthaus

    D. Cafu

18. Brazil v Sweden is one of the commonest matchups at the World Cup. How many times have the two sides met?

    A. 3

    B. 5

    C. 4

    D. 7

19. How many times have Argentina and Germany met in the final of the World Cup?

    A. 4

    B. 3

    C. 2

    D. 1

20. No World Cup match has seen as many goals as Austria's 7-5 victory over Switzerland. At which tournament did this match take place?

    A. 1950 World Cup

    B. 1954 World Cup

    C. 1958 World Cup

    D. 1962 World Cup

20 Trivia Answers

1. C – Argentina

2. B – Luxembourg

3. D – 64 years

4. C – 4

5. D – 7

6. B – Germany

7. C – Germany

8. D – Argentina

9. A – Mexico

10. A – Angola

11. D – France

12. D – England

13. B – Russia

14. C – Wales

15. B – Lucien Laurent

16. B – Paolo Maldini

17. B – Rafael Marquez

18. D – 7

19. B – 3

20. B – 1954 World Cup

10 Fun Facts

1. Five-time World Cup winners Brazil are the only team that has participated in all 21 previous editions of the famous tournament. Four-time winners Germany and Italy have taken part in 19 and 18 editions, respectively.

2. Brazil and Germany have played the most matches in the World Cup. Despite the fact that Germany has missed two previous editions of the tournament, they have played 109 World Cup matches, the same as Brazil.

3. Turkey striker Hakan Sukur's 11th-second opener against South Korea in the third-place playoff match at the 2002 World Cup is the fastest goal ever scored in the history of the FIFA World Cup.

4. Germany midfielder, Lothar Matthaus, has made more World Cup appearances than any other player. He played for his country 25 times across five tournaments between 1982 and 1998. His compatriot Miroslav Klose sits just behind him with 24 appearances across four tournaments.

5. Along with Germany's Lothar Matthaus, Mexicans Antonio Carbajal and Rafael Marquez are the only other players to have played at five different World Cup tournaments. Italy's Gianluigi Buffon was also part of five World Cup squads but did not make an appearance at the 1998 World Cup.

6. Germany striker, Miroslav Klose, broke the record for most World Cup goals during his country's 7-1 annihilation of Brazil at the 2014 World Cup semifinal. His 16th World Cup goal took him ahead of Brazil's Ronaldo, who until then held the record with 15 goals.

7. No player has scored as many goals in a single World Cup tournament as France's Just Fontaine. All of the Marrakech-born forward's 13 World Cup goals came at the 1958 World Cup in Sweden.

8. The five goals scored by Russian striker Oleg Salenko during his country's 6-1 win against Cameroon at the 1994 World Cup represent the most scored by any player in a single World Cup match.

9. Hungary's golden generation, arguably one of the best teams that never won a World Cup, scored a single tournament record of 27 goals on their way to finishing runners-up at the 1954 World Cup.

10. West Germany's Helmut Schon coached his country for a record 25 World Cup matches across four tournaments between 1966 and 1978, leading them to the title in 1974.

FINAL WHISTLE

Hello our fellow *football-lover*.

We really hope you enjoyed The Best World Cup Trivia Book Ever. And, congratulations on reading it to the end!

We create these books to allow football fans to expand their knowledge around their favourite clubs and players, but most importantly, to keep the passion we all have for the game lit and alive.

Life can come with many challenges and setbacks. But something that never leaves our side is our love for the game.

If you enjoyed reading this book, we'd like to kindly ask for your feedback and thoughts in the review section on Amazon.

This would really encourage us to keep creating the highest quality books and content for football fans across the globe.

Thanks in advance!

Ball out,

Made in United States
Orlando, FL
21 December 2022